Mathematics 1

Answer these questions.

a How much more does the bicycle cost than the scooter? _____

b Tom wants to buy the guitar. He has £8.
How much more does he need? _____

c Jane bought the doll's house. She has £3 left.
How much did she have to start with? _____

d Joe had £22. He bought the skates.
Can he buy the bicycle? _____

e Samina had £12. She bought the tennis racket and the
board game. How much had she left? _____

f Rhoda bought the bicycle. She had £4 left.
Did she have more than £25 to start with? _____

g Chris bought the football and the radio.
How much did he have left out of £15? _____

h Anne had £10, but she lost £5.
Can she buy the teddy bear? _____

i Ahmed has £20. Can he buy the scooter and the guitar? _____

j Liz has a £10 note and three £1 coins.
Can she buy the guitar? _____

k Renzo had £14. He bought the cricket bat.
Can he buy the guitar? _____

l Tim had £25. He bought the scooter and the guitar.
How much money did he have left? _____

Language Skills 1

By putting one letter in front of <u>eat</u> you can make several other words, for example: <u>beat</u> or <u>neat</u>.

Find the correct letter to put in front of each of these.
The word you make must fit the clue.

a	___ old ➡ fearless	**f**	___ ane ➡ a hollow stem
b	___ old ➡ not hot	**g**	___ ane ➡ a narrow road
c	___ old ➡ precious metal	**h**	___ ane ➡ long hair on the neck
d	___ old ➡ keep a grip	**i**	___ ane ➡ window glass
e	___ old ➡ exchanged for money	**j**	___ ane ➡ not mad

From the two words at the end of each sentence, choose the correct word to complete the sentence.

k Mum bought a bag of _____to make a cake. [flour, flower]

l The_____withered and died. [flour, flower]

m The car turned_____at the crossroads. [right, write]

n Please_____to me when you are away. [right, write]

o I think I have been_____before. [here, hear]

p From my room I could _____the sea. [here, hear]

q The front of_____house faces south. [there, their]

r _____ goes our last chance of scoring a goal. [There, Their]

Complete each word by writing **ou** or **ow**.

s	**t**	**u**

c _ _	h _ _ s e	c l _ _ d

v	**w**	**x**

_ _ _ l	m _ _ s e	fr _ _ n

page 4

Schofield&Sims

Homework **3**

For year 5

thinking writing

Mathematics Science

"Language skills"

reading and vocabulary

Mathematics writing

Sciencing

"Language skills"

thinking

reading

and vocabulary

writing

Name

Fill in the blanks with words from the list.

porridge	handful	eating	hammer	made	table
some	fire	woman	mean	pity	right
thought	opened	tasted	knocked	brought	again

a A hungry tramp_____ on the door of a cottage.

b He said to the woman who _____the door,
"Have you got anything to eat, please?"

c "No," said the_____.

d She had plenty, but she was_____.

e Then the tramp saw a hammer on the_____.

f "This hammer will do to make_____ ," he said.
"Nonsense!" said the woman.

g The tramp put the_____ into water in a pot on the _____.
He stirred and tasted.

h "A_____we have no salt."

i "Here, I have _____," said the woman.

j The tramp added the salt and_____it again.

k "Could do with a_____of oats and a little butter."

l The woman_____oats and butter.

m In they went, and the tramp tasted it_____.

n "Just_____," he said. "Try some." The woman tasted the porridge.

o "Well, well," she said, "I never_____ such good porridge could be
_____from a hammer."

p The tramp laughed and went on _____.

**In the space provided, write the words that describe the people
who live in the following countries, e.g. England *English*.**

q England_____ **r** France_____ **s** Scotland _____

t America_____ **u** Wales _____ **v** Spain   _____

w Ireland _____ **x** Italy   _____

Science 1

Read the passage.

We live on Planet Earth. There is more water than land on Earth's surface. Earth is really one huge ocean broken by islands. The biggest islands are called continents. The picture shows the Earth cut in half. The outer skin is called the crust. We live on Earth's crust. Beneath the crust, the Earth is a ball of hot rock and metal made up of three layers. Each layer is hotter than the one outside. The Earth's crust is made up of rocks and soil. Rocks are made of minerals. One of the very soft minerals is chalk. Diamond is a very hard mineral. Salt is a mineral that we eat. On Earth there are about 2000 different minerals.

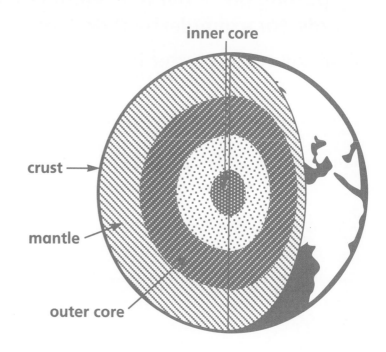

Read each sentence. Write 'T' if it is true. Write 'F' if it is false.

a There is more land than water on Earth. _____

b Continents are the biggest islands on Earth. _____

c The crust of Earth is the outer surface. _____

d The hottest part of Earth is the outer core. _____

e The layer which is the centre of Earth is called the inner core. _____

f In the rocks on Earth there are about 2000 different minerals. _____

g All minerals are hard. _____

h The inside of Earth is a ball of hot rock and metal. _____

Writing I

A joining word is called a **conjunction**.
for example, in this sentence "They waited and waited <u>but</u> the bus did not come."

<u>but</u> is a conjunction.

Join the following with conjunctions. Use each word in the box only once.

and	or	when	until	although	because

a You can have lemonade_____ there is some orange juice.

b We could watch a video _____we have dinner in an hour's time.

c Anne was startled _____the door burst open.

d You may not watch that programme_____ it is far too late.

e Put on some warm clothes_____then we will play in the snow.

f Our football team lost _____ every player did his best.

Write each sentence using capital letters and the correct punctuation.

g what time does the play start

_____

h olivia and edward brown are twins

_____

i the capital of france is paris

_____

j shall we take our holiday in june

_____

k i go swimming every friday morning

_____

l where did you go on easter sunday

_____

Thinking 1

Each picture in the bottom row is the result of one of the pictures in the top row. Match the letter of each top-row picture with the number of a bottom-row picture.

a 	b 	c 	d 

1	2 	3 	4 

a _____   b _____   c _____   d _____

Fill in the missing numbers.

e 10 8 __ 4 __

f 1 2 3 5 __ 7 9 10 __

g 1 4 7 __ 13 __

h 16 14 12 __ 8 __

i 11 22 33 __ 55 __

j 15 12 9 __ 3 __

**Which picture in each row is the odd one out?
Write the number of the picture.**

k | 1  | 2  | 3  | 4  |

The odd one out is _____

l | 1  | 2  | 3 | 4  |

The odd one out is _____

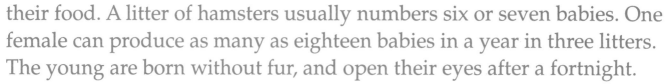

Reading and Vocabulary 2

Hamsters in the wild burrow more than two metres into the ground. They like to live alone.

Some people keep hamsters as pets. Usually just one hamster is kept in a cage. This is because they often fight when put together. Even males and females should be kept apart, except when they are being mated.

Female hamsters are bigger than the males. The females often attack the males and steal their food. A litter of hamsters usually numbers six or seven babies. One female can produce as many as eighteen babies in a year in three litters. The young are born without fur, and open their eyes after a fortnight.

Read each sentence.

Circle TRUE if it is true, and circle FALSE if it is false.

a	The hamster is a burrowing animal.	TRUE	FALSE
b	Hamsters like to live in groups.	TRUE	FALSE
c	Males and females should be put together only for mating.	TRUE	FALSE
d	The females are bigger than the males.	TRUE	FALSE
e	The males often attack the females.	TRUE	FALSE
f	A litter may number as many as eighteen babies.	TRUE	FALSE

Write down one word to describe each of the following.

g	a man who fits water-pipes	_____
h	a male sheep	_____
i	a building where films are shown	_____
j	a company of singers	_____
k	an animal's foot	_____
l	a strong desire for food	_____

Mathematics 2

A shape with five straight sides is called a pentagon.

a Colour in the shapes that are pentagons.

 1   2   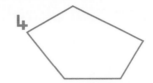 3   4   5    6

Below each clock face write the same time on the blank digital clock.

a.m.   a.m.   a.m.   a.m.

b    **c**    **d**    **e**

Write the missing numbers on the line.

f $3 \times 4 =$ _____   **g** $5 \times 2 =$ _____   **h** $6 \times$ _____ $= 12$

i $5 \times$ _____ $= 15$ **j** _____ $\times 3 = 21$ **k** $8 \times 2 =$ _____

l $4 \times$ _____ $= 20$ **m** $9 \times$ _____ $= 18$ **n** $6 \times$ _____ $= 24$

Below each shape write in words the part of the shape that is shaded. The first one is done for you.

o

one third

p

_____

q

_____

r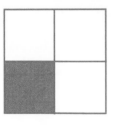

_____

s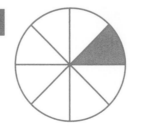

_____

t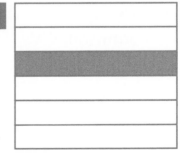

_____

page 9

Language Skills 2

Singular means one only. Plural means more than one, for example:

Singular: boy   Plural: boys   Singular: woman   Plural: women

Change these words to the plural.

a jug _____   **b** man _____   **c** hand _____

d door _____   **e** foot _____   **f** city _____

g fox _____   **h** tooth _____   **i** match _____

Change these words to the singular.

j chips _____   **k** pennies_____   **l** leaves _____

m children_____   **n** boxes _____   **o** ladies _____

In the names of the objects are four pairs of rhymes.
Complete the rhyming pairs.

p mug and _____   **q** fish and _____

r moon and _____   **s** thistle and _____

People's names are listed in alphabetical order by their surnames.
Other names or initials are placed after surnames in
alphabetical order.

For example,

Hardy, T S
Hardy, Walter B
Johnson, C V

Arrange this list in alphabetical order.

t Thomas, J T _____
Benson, John S _____
Willis, R V _____
Thomas, Sean W _____
Harris, W P _____
Willis, A L _____
Thomas, B R _____

After each part there are two words.
Write the correct word in the space in the sentence.

a There are places where there are cracks in the Earth's crust. These cracks divide the _____ into parts. **[soil/crust]**

b Each of these _____ is called a plate. **[parts/cracks]**

c In most places there is solid rock over the _____ . **[cracks/earth]**

d At times the plates slide in opposite _____ . **[colliding/directions]**

e The _____ may scrape together. **[plates/cracks]**

f Sometimes the plates _____ and collide. **[stop/move]**

g The solid rocks above the _____ break and move. This is called an earthquake. **[cracks/plates]**

h Under the Earth's crust there is red-hot melted _____ and soil. **[soil/rock]**

i Sometimes this moves up towards the _____ . **[crust/mantle]**

j It tries to find a _____ spot in the crust. **[strong/weak]**

k When it does, it pours out molten _____ called lava. **[rock/steam]**

l This usually piles up above the Earth's crust in the shape of a _____ . **[square/cone]**

m Then it _____ and hardens. **[cools/warms]**

n A new _____ has been born. **[mountain/volcano]**

o _____ volcanoes are active. **[Some/No]**

p From time to time fresh lava, _____ gases and steam pour out of the crater. **[hot/cold]**

q Some _____ are not active. **[gases/volcanoes]**

Writing 2

Write each sentence in the plural. The first one is started for you.

a The girl is riding a bicycle.

_____The girls_____

b The woman takes her child to school.

_____

c Please give me something to eat.

_____

d The army attacks at dawn.

_____

e The book was ruined out in the rain.

_____

f The lady was frightened by the mouse.

_____

Strong feeling is shown by an exclamation mark (!).

The house is on fire!   What a lovely present!

Look at the pictures below and read the captions.
Some of the captions need exclamation marks, and some do not.
Put a full stop or an exclamation mark after each caption.

g Help me___

h Don't touch___

i Look out___

j Don't touch___

k Look out___

l Help me___

Thinking 2

Write each kind of food from the list under its correct heading.

a

cheese	beans	herring	peas	cream
ham	pears	bananas	cod	lamb
mackerel	cabbage	plums	haddock	yoghurt
turkey	carrots	milk	chicken	lemons
oranges	potatoes	plaice	beef	butter

Meat	Fish	Vegetables	Fruit	Dairy products

b Write these dates in their correct order in the year.
The first one has been done for you.

2 JUN	8 DEC	5 APR	28 JAN	13 APR

__28 JAN__ _____ _____ _____ _____

c Begin at any letter. Follow the lines and spell the name of a boy or girl. Do not skip letters. Find and write the names of the six boys and girls.

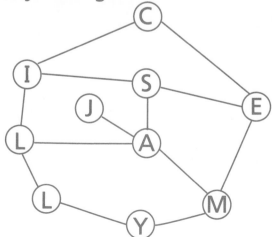

_____

_____

_____

_____

_____

_____

Reading and Vocabulary 3

There were horses on Earth more than fifty million years ago. The earliest ancestor of the horse was the size of a fox. The horse used its speed to escape its many enemies. But the cavemen hunted and killed the horse for food. They made no attempt to tame or ride the

horse. It is supposed that the horse was first used about four thousand years ago by a tribe living in Central Asia. They trained the horse to pull heavy loads. But we do not know who were the first people to ride horses.

For centuries special types of horses have been bred for particular jobs. Great draught-horses are bred for strength and staying-power. Horses used in horse-racing are bred for speed. Now that engines are doing the hard work for us, the horse is mainly used for our pleasure. We enjoy the horse for show-jumping, racing and pony-trekking.

Answer these questions.

a How long have horses been on Earth?

_____

b What size was the earliest ancestor of the horse?

_____

c Did early horses have any enemies?

_____

d What did the horse use to escape its enemies?

_____

e Did cavemen tame or ride the horse?

_____

f Who first trained horses to pull heavy loads?

_____

g Do we know who first rode horses?

_____

What words in the passage have these meanings?

h to get free _____   **i** hundreds of years _____

j raised _____   **k** a thousand thousand _____

l to try _____   **m** machines that provide power _____

page **14**

HOMEWORK BOOK 3 ANSWERS

Note for users

Taking an interest in the child's work is of great importance. Take every opportunity to praise work that is correct, and offer help and advice where the child experiences difficulty. Make sure that the child understands the instructions which introduce each exercise. Some children experience more difficulty with the instructions than with the work itself.

There are advantages in allowing the child to mark his or her own work. This informs the child of the correct answer in cases where mistakes have occurred. It is important to look again at answers that are wrong and for the child to discover why an answer is incorrect so that he or she can learn as a result of the error.

Where a weakness is revealed, further similar exercises can be provided to give the child more practice and confidence.

A child should not be expected to undertake too much work in a short time. The exercises should be well spaced out so that the last pages are being worked towards the end of the appropriate school year.

Reading and Vocabulary 1

a knocked	**b** opened	**c** woman
d mean	**e** table	**f** porridge
g hammer, fire	**h** pity	**i** some
j tasted	**k** handful	**l** brought
m again	**n** right	**o** thought, made
p eating		
q English	**r** French	**s** Scottish
t American	**u** Welsh	**v** Spanish
w Irish	**x** Italian	

Mathematics 1

a £9	**b** £4	**c** £21
d No	**e** £7	**f** No
g £4	**h** No	**i** No
j Yes	**k** No	**l** £2

Language Skills 1

a bold	**b** cold	**c** gold
d hold	**e** sold	**f** cane
g lane	**h** mane	**i** pane
j sane		
k flour	**l** flower	**m** right
n write	**o** here	**p** hear
q their	**r** There	
s cow	**t** house	**u** cloud
v owl	**w** mouse	**x** frown

Science 1

a F	**b** T	**c** T	**d** F
e T	**f** T	**g** F	**h** T

Writing 1

a or	**b** until	**c** when
d because	**e** and	**f** although

g What time does the play start?
h Olivia and Edward Brown are twins.
i The capital of France is Paris.
j Shall we take our holiday in June?
k I go swimming every Friday morning.
l Where did you go on Easter Sunday?

Thinking 1

a 3	**b** 1	**c** 4	**d** 2
e 6, 2			
f 6, 11			
g 10, 16			
h 10, 6			
i 44, 66			
j 6, 0			
k 2			
l 3			

Reading and Vocabulary 2

a True	**b** False	**c** True
d True	**e** False	**f** False
g plumber	**h** ram	**i** cinema
j choir	**k** paw	**l** hunger

Mathematics 2

a 2, 4, 5, 6	**b** 9:30	**c** 2:45
d 7:25	**e** 11:10	
f 12	**g** 10	**h** 2
i 3	**j** 7	**k** 16
l 5	**m** 2	**n** 4
o one third	**p** one fifth	**q** one half
r one quarter	**s** one eighth	**t** one sixth

Language Skills 2

a jugs	**b** men	**c** hands
d doors	**e** feet	**f** cities
g foxes	**h** teeth	**i** matches
j chip	**k** penny	**l** leaf
m child	**n** box	**o** lady
p mug and jug		**q** fish and dish
r moon and spoon		**s** thistle and whistle

t Benson, John S;
Harris, W P;
Thomas, B R;
Thomas, J T;
Thomas, Sean W;
Willis, A L;
Willis, R V

Science 2

a crust	**b** parts	**c** cracks
d directions	**e** plates	**f** move
g cracks	**h** rock	**i** crust
j weak	**k** rock	**l** cone
m cools	**n** volcano	**o** Some
p hot	**q** volcanoes	

Writing 2

a The girls are riding bicycles.
b The women take their children to school.
c Please give us something to eat.
d The armies attack at dawn.
e The books were ruined out in the rain.
f The ladies were frightened by the mice.
g Help me!   h Don't touch.
i Look out.   j Don't touch!
k Look out!   l Help me.

Thinking 2

a

MEAT	FISH	VEGETAB-LES	FRUIT	DAIRY PRODUCTS
ham	herring	beans	pears	cheese
lamb	cod	peas	bananas	cream
turkey	mackerel	cabbage	plums	yoghurt
chicken	haddock	carrots	lemons	milk
beef	plaice	potatoes	oranges	butter

b 28 JAN, 5 APR, 13 APR, 2 JUN, 8 DEC
c Sally, Amy, James, Lisa, Sam, Alice

Reading and Vocabulary 3

a more than fifty million years
b the size of a fox
c Yes   d its speed   e No
f A tribe living in Central Asia.
g No   h escape   i centuries
j bred   k million   l attempt
m engines

Mathematics 3

a 5 cm   b 4 cm   c 8 cm
d 3 cm   e 10 cm   f 1 cm
g top   6 cm
   bottom   6 cm
   left side   7 cm
   right side   7 cm
                26 cm
   The perimeter of the shape is 26 centimetres.
h 12   i 18   j 20
k 21   l 20   m 24

Language Skills 3

a deer   b beard   c beer   d cheer
e ear   f tear   g steer   h spear
i Where   j What   k Whose   l Why
m Which   n Who   o When
p Lauren and Natalie were playing tennis.
q A lion was in the cage.
r The children have had enough to eat.
s There are oranges in the bowl.

Science 3

a round   b animals   c Earth
d space   e down   f magnet
g force   h gravity   i works
j away   k towards   l Rivers
m hill   n pulled   o possible

Writing 3

a In my uncle's garden there are apples, pears, plums, strawberries and cherries.
b After school I walked home with Jack, Ahmed, Alison, Gary and Laura.
c To make cauliflower cheese you need flour, butter, milk, cheese and cauliflower.
d For my birthday I was given an action man, a computer game, Monopoly, two books and a watch.
e The circle is inside the square.
f A girl is on the swing.
g You need a saw to cut wood.

Thinking 3

a drink   b house   c push
d ugly   e cunning   f relaxed
g shop   h find   i land
j fight
k 4, 2, 6, 1, 5, 3
l hear   m shoe   n rails
o burrow   p bat

Reading and Vocabulary 4

a favoured, approved
b early   c unpopular   d long/tall
e lucky   f released   g accepted/
h disappeared   i young/new   allowed
j T   k F
l F   m T

Mathematics 4

a 35 b 40 c 42
d 42 e 53 f 53
g 81 h 94 i 90
j 91

k 5 x 2 = 10   l 9 x 2 = 18   m 1 x 13 = 13
3 x 2 = 6   7 x 3 = 21   9 x 2 = 18
4 x 1 = 4   1 x 1 = 1   7 x 4 = 28
                               5 x 2 = 10
Total 20   Total 40   Total 69

n 18 o 28 p 35 q 11
r 27 s 7   t 19 u 48

Language Skills 4

a	big	bigger	biggest
b	high	higher	highest
c	sad	sadder	saddest
d	late	later	latest
e	deep	deeper	deepest
f	happy	happier	happiest
g	greedy	greedier	greediest
h	bad	worse	worst

i camel   j petrol   k tunnel   l barrel
m medal   n sandal   o stencil   p pedal
q rabbit, city, road, river, rat, tower, bin, honey

Science 4

a the atmosphere   b gravity
c nitrogen and oxygen d oxygen
e nitrogen   f clouds
g 500 kilometres   h space

Writing 4

a Mum said Spot needed a bath.
She half-filled the a bath with water.
Spot howled as we lifted him into the bath.
Mum soaped him all over.
Then she let the dirty water out of the bath.
Next we had to rinse the soap off Spot.
Spot howled again when we held him under the shower to rinse him.
When we had finished, Spot jumped out of the bath.
He shook himself all over us.
Spot, Mum and I were wet all over.

Thinking 4

a New Year's Day, Good Friday, Easter Sunday, August Bank Holiday, Hallowe'en, Christmas Day, Boxing Day, New Year's Eve.
b cereal and milk, snakes and ladders, ice-cream and cornet, paint brush and paint, dog and bone, bucket and spade.
c ATTACK AT DAWN

Reading and Vocabulary 5

A farmer who worked in his **fields** always hid his dinner in a hollow **tree**. One day a fox saw what he did. The fox waited **until** the farmer had gone away. Then, by pulling in his sides, the fox **managed** to squeeze into the tree. Once **inside**, the fox began eating the food. He ate and **ate** until he could eat no more. Then the fox tried to **squeeze** himself out of the tree. But he could **not** do so. No way could he drag his **plump** stomach through the hole.

The trapped fox began to **howl** for help. A **friend** heard him and came running "Help me!" **pleaded** the fox from inside the tree. "I've **eaten** so much that I cannot get through the hole." His friend said, "There is only one **thing** you can do. You'll have to **wait** until you grow thin enough to get out again.

Learn this **lesson** for the future: think before you act.

b girl   c princess
d aunt   e daughter
f actress   g female
h sister   i her

Mathematics 5

a
X	2	4	6	8
2	4	8	12	16
3	6	12	18	24
4	8	16	24	32
5	10	20	30	40

b
X	3	5	7	9
1	3	5	7	9
3	9	15	21	27
6	18	30	42	54
7	21	35	49	63

c
X	10	6	3	2
8	80	48	24	16
5	50	30	15	10
2	20	12	6	4
0	0	0	0	0

d
X	9	10	0	4
4	36	40	0	16
9	81	90	0	36
1	9	10	0	4
7	63	70	0	28

e 54   f 7   g 15
h 46   i 80p   j 20p
k 6   l 35 minutes m 30 cm
n 8 + 3

Mathematics 3

Measure each line in centimetres.
Write the answer in the box after the line.

a _____ [ ] cm

b _____ [ ] cm

c _____ [ ] cm

d _____ [ ] cm

e _____ [ ] cm

f __ [ ] cm

The distance around something is called the **perimeter**.

Find the perimeter of this shape. Measure the length of each side.
Add the four lengths to find the perimeter.

g

top _____ cm

bottom _____ cm

left side _____ cm

right side _____ cm

_____

_____ cm

The perimeter of the shape
is _____ centimetres.

Write the answers to these sums.

h
```
    4
    6
+   2
_____
```

i
```
    7
    3
+   8
_____
```

j
```
    9
    3
+   8
_____
```

k
```
    8
    7
+   6
_____
```

l
```
    7
    5
+   8
_____
```

m
```
    8
    9
+   7
_____
```

Language Skills 3

Complete each word by writing **ea** or **ee**.

a	b	c	d

d _ _ r	b _ _ r d	b _ _ r	c h _ _ r

e	f	g	h

_ _ r	t _ _ r	s t _ _ r	s p _ _ r

Choose the correct word from the panel to begin each of these questions.

What	When
Where	Which
Who	Whose
Why	

i _____ do flies go during the winter?

j _____ shall we get Dad for Christmas?

k _____ coat is this on my peg?

l _____ are you sitting out in the rain?

m _____ would you prefer, ice-cream or cabbage?

n _____ will help me with my homework?

o _____ will you return this book to the library?

The words in brackets are not correct.
Write the corrected sentence on the line.

p Lauren and Natalie (was) playing tennis.

_____

q A lion (were) in the cage.

_____

r The children (has) had enough to eat.

_____

s There (is) oranges in the bowl.

_____

Science 3

down	Rivers	magnet	animals	space
away	possible	towards	hill	force
pulled	round	Earth	works	gravity

a The Earth is a great _____ ball spinning through space.

b All over the Earth are people, _____ , plants, soil, water, rocks and air.

c How do they all stay on _____ ?

d Why do they not fall off the Earth into _____ ?

e The Earth tries to pull everything _____ to its centre.

f It acts like a _____ .

g This _____ is called gravity.

h When you jump up, _____ pulls you down.

i Gravity _____ all round the world.

j Wherever you are, <u>up</u> is _____ from Earth.

k <u>Down</u> is _____ the world.

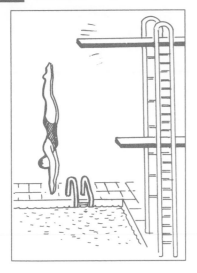

l _____ flow down the mountains.

m A ball always runs down a _____ .

n Rain and snow are _____ from the sky to Earth.

o Gravity pulls things as near as _____ to the centre of the Earth.

Items in a list are separated by a comma or an 'and'.
The last two items are usually separated by an 'and'.

For example: Our Christmas dinner consisted of soup, turkey, three vegetables, trifle <u>and</u> coffee.

Copy the sentences below, putting in a comma or an 'and' to separate the items in the list.

a In my uncle's garden there are apples pears plums strawberries cherries.

_____

b After school I walked home with Jack Ahmed Alison Gary Laura.

_____

c To make cauliflower cheese you need flour butter milk cheese cauliflower.

_____

_____

d For my birthday I was given an action man a computer game Monopoly two books a watch.

_____

_____

Rearrange the words below to make a sentence to match each picture. The first word of the sentence begins with a capital letter.

e inside square The is the circle.

_____

f the girl swing A is on.

_____

g cut saw You a need wood to.

_____

Thinking 3

Write the word which does not belong.

a sad   happy   cheerful   drink   grumpy   _____

b tall   small   house   wide   narrow   _____

c push   end   finish   halt   stop   _____

d giant   huge   ugly   gigantic   vast   _____

e clever   bright   gifted   cunning   expert   _____

f excited   relaxed   merry   joyful   gleeful   _____

g socks   shoes   shop   hat   anorak   _____

h hunt   seek   find   track   search   _____

i fall   drop   plunge   tumble   land   _____

j fight   injure   wound   hurt   cripple   _____

---

k **These pictures are in the wrong order.**
Write the numbers of the pictures in their correct order.

_____   _____   _____   _____   _____   _____

Write the word from the brackets that fits each blank.

l Eye is to see as ear is to _____ . [head, hear, know, talk]

m Hand is to glove as foot is to _____ . [walk, shoe, ankle, feet]

n Car is to road as train is to _____ . [station, wheels, rails, engine]

o Bird is to nest as rabbit is to _____ . [burrow, lair, set, perch]

p Tennis is to racket as cricket is to _____ . [ball, wicket, bails, bat]

Reading and Vocabulary 4

Late in the 19th century, clockwork toy bears were being made. Bears which could drink, dance or smoke were popular. But the teddy bear, as we know it, came about in a strange way.

In 1902 Teddy Roosevelt was President of the United States of America. One day he took a short holiday to go on a bear hunt. The President was unlucky. His only chance to make a kill was a bear that had been captured. The bear was tied to a tree. Teddy Roosevelt was invited to shoot it. The President refused.

The story was told in a newspaper. A cartoon showed Teddy Roosevelt with his gun, and the bear he had saved. More cartoons of the bear appeared. Within a year, the cartoon bear had been made into a toy for children. Now the teddy bear is popular with both children and grown-ups. Some people collect teddy bears of all shapes and sizes. Some old teddy bears are worth a great deal of money. Teddy bear fairs are held all over the country.

a **Teddy bears are popular. Circle two of the following words that have a similar meaning to 'popular'.**

accepted   favoured   approved   disliked

Write the words that are opposite in meaning to the following:

b late   _____   **c** popular   _____

d short   _____   **e** unlucky   _____

f captured   _____   **g** refused   _____

h appeared   _____   **i** old   _____

Write 'T' if a sentence is true, and 'F' if it is false.

j The 'teddy bear' is named after Teddy Roosevelt.   _____

k A 'cartoon' is another name for a photograph.   _____

l The President shot a bear that had been captured.   _____

m People got to know the story of the President
and the bear because it was in a newspaper.   _____

Mathematics 4

Write your answers on the dotted lines.

a
```
  16
+ 19
```
....

b
```
  18
+ 22
```
....

c
```
  14
+ 28
```
....

d
```
  23
+ 19
```
....

e
```
  36
+ 17
```
....

f
```
  28
+ 25
```
....

g
```
  44
+ 37
```
....

h
```
  57
+ 37
```
....

i
```
  67
+ 23
```
....

j
```
  73
+ 18
```
....

Complete the first problem. Then work on the other problems.

k The Brown family love bananas. Last week Mum and Dad ate 5 each. Their two sons ate 3 each, and their daughter ate 4. How many bananas did the whole family eat last week?

5 x 2 = _____

3 x 2 = _____

4 x 1 = _____

Total _____

l Dad bought Mum a box of chocolates. Mum and Dad ate 9 chocolates each. Their 3 children ate 7 each. The dog knocked the box off the settee and ate the last chocolate. How many chocolates had been in the box?

_____ = _____

_____ = _____

_____ = _____

Total _____

m In our street we had a competition to see who could collect the most badges. The winner collected 13 badges. Two boys collected 9 badges each. Two girls and 2 boys collected 7 badges each. A girl and a boy collected 5 each. How many badges were collected altogether?

_____ = _____

_____ = _____

_____ = _____

_____ = _____

Total _____

Write the answers to each of these.

n
```
  24
-  6
```
....

o
```
  35
-  7
```
....

p
```
  41
-  6
```
....

q
```
  23
- 12
```
....

r
```
  69
- 42
```
....

s
```
  23
- 16
```
....

t
```
  53
- 34
```
....

u
```
  71
- 23
```
....

page 21

Complete this table.

a	big	bigger	biggest
b	high		highest
c	sad	sadder	
d		later	latest
e	deep		
f		happier	
g	greedy		
h	bad		worst

Complete each word by writing <u>el</u>, <u>al</u>, <u>il</u> or <u>ol</u>.

i   cam _ _

j   petr _ _

k    tunn _ _

l   barr _ _

m   med _ _

n    sand _ _

o   stenc _ _

p   ped _ _

q A word used as a name is called a noun.
For example, <u>girl</u>, <u>town</u> and <u>pen</u> are nouns.

Which of the words in the panel are nouns? Write them below.

rabbit	smooth	quickly	city	road
because	clean	river	thin	rat
tower	bin	young	easy	honey

Nouns: _____

_____

Read the passage.

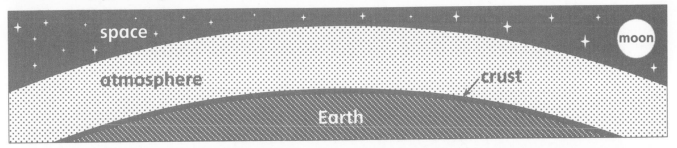

The whole Earth is wrapped in a covering of air. This is called the atmosphere. The air is kept close to the Earth by the force of gravity. This stops the air drifting off into space.

Air is a mixture of gases. The two main gases are nitrogen and oxygen. About a fifth of air is oxygen. This is the gas our bodies need. In air there is almost four times as much nitrogen as oxygen. There are tiny amounts of other gases. This mixture of gases is just right for all living things on Earth.

Also in the atmosphere are water vapour and dust. These come together to make clouds.

As you go higher and higher in the atmosphere, the air gets thinner and thinner. Above 500km the atmosphere gradually merges into space.

Read each question. Write your answer on the line.

a What do we call the covering of air round Earth? _____

b What stops the air drifting off into space? _____

c What are the two main gases in air? _____

d Which gas is needed by our bodies? _____

e Which is the main gas in air? _____

f When water vapour and dust come
together, what do they make? _____

g Above what height does the atmosphere merge into space? _____

h What is above the atmosphere? _____

The pictures below tell a story. But the sentences below the pictures are in the wrong order.

Write the sentences in their correct order in the space given.

Spot howled again when we held him under the shower to rinse him.

Mum soaped him all over.

Next we had to rinse the soap off Spot.

Spot, Mum and I were wet all over.

Mum said Spot needed a bath.

He shook himself all over us.

Then she let the dirty water out of the bath.

Spot howled as we lifted him into the bath.

When we had finished, Spot jumped out of the bath.

She half-filled the bath with water.

_____

_____

_____

_____

_____

_____

_____

_____

_____

Thinking 4

The names of the following days in the year are in the wrong order. Write the days in their correct order in the year.

a
Christmas Day   _____

Good Friday   _____

New Year's Eve   _____

Easter Sunday   _____

Boxing Day   _____

August Bank Holiday   _____

New Year's Day   _____

Hallowe'en   _____

b Look at the pictures. There are six pairs that go together. Write down the names of the six pairs.

_____   _____

_____   _____

_____   _____

c In a secret code A = B, B = C, C = D, etc.
Decode this message and write it down.

BUUBDL BU EBXO ➡ _____

a Fill the blanks with words from the list.

managed	thing	inside	pleaded	fields	wait
squeeze	lesson	eaten	ate	plump	not
howl	tree	until	friend		

A farmer who worked in his _____ always hid his dinner in a hollow _____. One day a fox saw what he did. The fox waited _____ the farmer had gone away. Then, by pulling in his sides, the fox _____ to squeeze into the tree. Once _____, the fox began eating the food. He ate and _____ until he could eat no more. Then the fox tried to _____ himself out of the tree. But he could _____ do so. No way could he drag his _____ stomach through the hole.

The trapped fox began to _____ for help. A _____ heard him and came running. "Help me!" _____ the fox from inside the tree. "I've _____ so much that I cannot get through the hole." His friend said, "There is only one _____ you can do. You'll have to _____ until you grow thin enough to get out again.

Learn this _____ for the future: think before you act."

Change the following words to the feminine. One is done for you.

b boy _____girl_____

c prince _____

d uncle _____

e son _____

f actor _____

g male _____

h brother _____

i him _____

Mathematics 5

Write the missing numbers in each table.

a

X	2	4	6	8
2				
3	6			
4				
5				

b

X	3	5	7	9
1		5		
3				
6				
7			49	

c

X	10	6	3	2
8				
5	50			
2				
0				0

d

X	9	10	0	4
4		40		
9				
1		10		
7			0	

e 9 more than 45 is _____

f How many hours from 8 a.m. to 3 p.m. ? _____

g How many 20p coins in £3? _____

h What is 8 less than 54? _____

i Share £2·40 equally among 3 children.
How much does each child get? _____

j A string of 8 sausages costs £1·60.
How much does each sausage cost? _____

k How many half-litre jugs can you fill
from a 3-litre milk container? _____

l Janice leaves home at 3:40 and arrives at
her aunt's house at 4:15. How long does
the journey take? _____

m How much longer than 70 centimetres is a metre? _____

n Which is smaller, 3 x 4 or 8 + 3? _____

Schofield & Sims

the long-established educational publisher
specialising in maths, English and science materials for schools

Aiming to make homework a positive learning experience, the **Homework** activity books reinforce children's learning in the core subjects (literacy, maths and science) and help to develop their cross-curricular thinking skills through enjoyable practice activities. Pull-out answers make marking quick and easy, and give children the chance to evaluate their own progress.

The **Homework** books support the Primary Frameworks for literacy and mathematics and the National Curriculum for science at Key Stage 2.

Homework Book 3 includes:

- **Literacy** – reading comprehension, nouns, adjectives, plurals, spelling
- **Maths** – money, 2-D shapes, fractions, number problems, vertical addition and subtraction (with borrowing/carrying), multiplication squares
- **Science** – the Earth and what it is made of, the Earth's atmosphere, gravity.

The full range of titles in the series is as follows:

Homework Book 1 for Year 3 pupils (7 & 8 year olds)   ISBN 978 07217 0845 4

Homework Book 2 for Year 4 pupils (8 & 9 year olds)   ISBN 978 07217 0846 1

Homework Book 3 for Year 5 pupils (9 & 10 year olds)   ISBN 978 07217 0851 5

Homework Book 4 for Year 6 pupils (10 & 11 year olds)   ISBN 978 07217 0852 2

Have you tried **More Homework** by Schofield & Sims?
This series gives children further practice in core subjects, ensuring that their essential skills and understanding are secure.

**For further information and to place your order
visit www.schofieldandsims.co.uk or telephone 01484 607080**

First edition copyright © Schofield and Sims Ltd, 1998
Seventeenth impression 2012
Author: Chris Burgess

Chris Burgess has asserted his moral right under the Copyright Designs and Patents Act, 1988 to be identified as the author of this work.

Printed in the UK by Wyndeham Gait Ltd, Grimsby, Lincolnshire

FSC MIX Paper from responsible sources FSC® C022534

ISBN 978-07217-0851-5

9 780721 708515

Schofield & Sims

Dogley Mill, Fenay Bridge, Huddersfield HD8 0NQ
Phone: 01484 607080 Facsimile: 01484 606815
E-mail: sales@schofieldandsims.co.uk

ISBN 978 07217 0851 5

**£2.95
(Retail price)**

Key Stage 2
Age range: 7–11 years